Timesave
Picture Prompts

Gwen Berwick and Sydney Thorne

Teacher's reference key

Time

A small clock on each page
tells you approximately
how long each activity should take.

Level

The number of stars on each page tells you the level of each activity.

Students with one or more years of English

Students with two or more years of English

Students with three or more years of English

Contents

Grammar cross-reference

Grammar	Title	Level	Page
Present simple (receptive)	On the planet Mago	★	52
Present simple	Spot the difference	★★	62
Present simple	London through the ages	★★★	88
Past simple (receptive)	Jennifer Lopez	★	30
Past simple (receptive)	Princess Diana	★★	32
Past simple	A Saturday in Brighton	★★	16
Past simple	Johnny Depp	★★★	22
Past simple questions	Britney Spears	★★★	23
Past simple	A school trip	★★	34
Past simple with negatives	Karen's visit to Britain	★★★	36
Past simple	The man with no memory	★★★	40
Past simple	Sarah, the scarf and the star	★★★	42
Past simple	Football reporter	★★★	72
Past simple	A strange story	★★★	85
Past simple	Reporting a bank robbery	★★★	86
Past simple	London through the ages	★★★	88
Past continuous	Murder in the flats	★★★	26
Present perfect	Are you a good detective?	★★	20
have been -ing	Mystery activities!	★★	18
Imperatives	Recipe: Lemon meringue pie	★★	54
going to	Accidents waiting to happen	★★★	28
-ing form	A holiday in Devon	★	10
like + -ing	Holiday postcards	★	74
like + -ing	A school for wizards	★★	78
Passive	The Titanic	★★★	24
Passive	Reporting a bank robbery	★★★	86
Adjectives	Adverts you love and hate	★	58
Adjectives	Test your powers of communication!	★★★	70
Adjectives	Formula 1	★	76
Adjectives	A school for wizards	★★	78
Adjectives and adverbs	The fun run	★★	12
Comparatives	Test your powers of communication!	★★★	70
Superlatives	Manchester United	★★	14
Prepositions of movement	The assault course	★	8
Prepositions of place	Spy-catcher	★★	66
Prepositions of place	Test your powers of communication!	★★★	70
Questions (receptive)	Mystery boy	★★★	84
Questions	A day out in York	★★	64
Questions	Twenty questions	★★	68
there is, there are/aren't any	The fashion boutique	★	6

Introduction

Timesaver Picture Prompts is a rich resource of lively photocopiable materials for English teachers to use with secondary school students aged 10–15. The easy-to-use materials and full answer key save preparation time and form an ideal bank of supplementary materials to complement any course book.

Motivating students

At *Mary Glasgow Magazines*, we believe that motivation is the key to success. *Timesaver Picture Prompts* is designed to engage students in several ways:
- through a wide range of reading, writing and speaking tasks, from recipes and picture stories to reporting a football match.
- through attractive and appealing photographs and artwork in a variety of styles.
- through contexts which appeal to young people, both girls and boys, such as profiles of celebrities, Manchester United football club, designer clothes and fast cars.
- through a variety of lively activities including puzzles, quizzes and pairwork games.
- through guided activities which help students achieve realistic goals successfully – nothing motivates more than success!

Developing students' skills

Timesaver Picture Prompts gives practice in a range of areas: two of the sections focus specifically on vocabulary and key grammar points, while others develop writing skills such as narrative and description. A variety of texts provide reading practice and there is a section specifically dedicated to speaking activities.

Preparation for exams

The varied practice offered in *Timesaver Picture Prompts* helps to prepare students for formal exams. For example, many of the activities address the requirements of the Cambridge PET exam that candidates 'must be able to give information, report events, describe situations and express opinions'.

How to use *Timesaver Picture Prompts*

The worksheets can be photocopied for use in the classroom and many are also suitable for self-study and homework.

Materials are presented mainly in two-page spreads: the two sheets in each spread are labelled A and B.

Stars indicate the level of the sheets:

★	students with 1 year of English
★★	students with 2 years of English
★★★	students with 3–4 years of English

A

The fashion boutique

① **Look at the two pictures on sheet B. Note the differences in Picture B. Then write what's different in Picture B.**

In Picture B ...

1 there is *a mirror on the wall*	6 there ....
2 there are some	7 ....
3 there isn't	8 ....
4 there aren't any	9 ....
5 there	10 ....

② **Colour the shapes that contain words of things you see in Pictures A and B. You will see what Sharon bought in the boutique!**

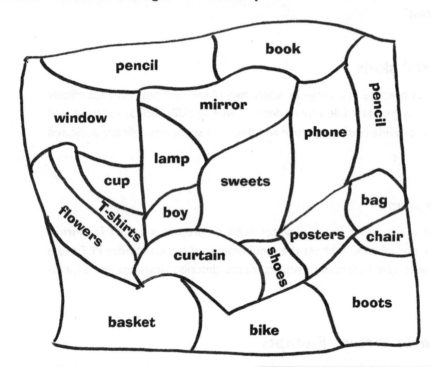

book · pencil · mirror · pencil · window · phone · lamp · cup · sweets · bag · flowers · T-shirts · boy · posters · chair · curtain · shoes · boots · basket · bike

Sharon bought a .... **.**

③ **Two puzzles**

1 Can you write a clothes word on each line?

H	A	T				
P	Y	J	A	M	A	S

2 Now write two more clothes words by changing one letter in each line.

S	K	I	R	T	S
S	▼				S
S		▼			S

The assault course

1 **Can you complete the assault course? Look at the pictures 1–7 on sheet B and complete the sentences with a preposition from the box.**

across
along
~~between~~
down
from
into
over
~~through~~
to
under
up

The Berrydown Assault Course

▶ **Please follow these instructions:**

1 First you go ......*through*...... the pipe.

2 Then you swing .... tree .... tree.

3 After that, jump .... the stream.

4 Next, crawl .... the tree.

5 Now jump .... the river and swim .... it.

6 Then walk .... the tree trunk.

7 Finally, climb .... the net and slide .... the other side.

Warning! You mustn't stop ..*between*.. **the different activities!**

2 **Look at the pictures on sheet B. Who is speaking? Write the numbers 1–5 next to each speech bubble.**

a My arms are getting tired! How many more trees are there?

Number ....

b Brr! This water's freezing.

Number ....

c I hope I don't get my feet wet!

Number ....

d Ooh! It's dark in here.

Number ....

e Ouch! My head!

Number ....

3 **What do you think the teenager in picture 6 is saying? Write a speech bubble for him!**

....
....
....

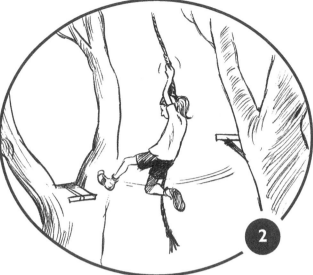

A

A holiday in Devon

1 A youth hostel in Devon has a programme of activities. Look at the programme, then look at the photos **A–I** on sheet **B**. Match the photos to the activities and write the letter(s) of the photo. This will give you Saturday's activity. Add it to the programme!

Programme of activities			
Monday	morning:	Sailing on the river Dart	....../... .....M.....
	afternoon:	Fishing by the river	....
Tuesday	morning:	Sightseeing trip round Plymouth	....
	afternoon:	Pony-trekking on Dartmoor	....
Wednesday	morning:	Ice-skating in Plymouth	....
	afternoon:	Free for shopping in Plymouth	....
Thursday	all day:	Birdwatching on Lundy Island	....
Friday		A choice of: Surfing in Newquay　　OR	....
		Canoeing on the river Dart	....
Saturday		....	

2 Now complete the word webs with the activities from Exercise 1.

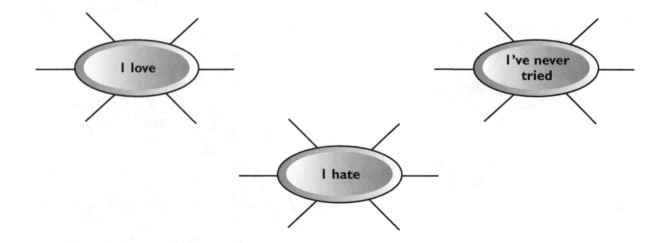

3 Can you add more activities (e.g. swimming, sunbathing) to the word webs?

A

The fun run

● ●

Information

In a fun run, the runners raise money for a charity if they complete the race.
There's a great atmosphere and some runners even run in fancy dress!

1 **Paul has written about a fun run. Read what he wrote and circle the correct words (adjectives or adverbs) in each sentence.**

A The crowd cheered *loud / loudly* when we started. I had a *good / well* start and ran quite fast.

B It was cold when we met up, so I wore my *warm / warmly* tracksuit. Exhibition Square was *absolute / absolutely* packed with people.

C There was the finishing line at last! I was *real / really* *happy / happily* to finish, but I was *complete / completely* exhausted.

D Then I passed a runner who was dressed up as a knight. His costume was very *heavy / heavily*, so of course he was quite *slow / slowly*.

E We ran past a band outside the church. They were playing *loud / loudly* music. Somebody was dressed as a bear; he was *amazing / amazingly* fast!

F Outside a big department store, I slipped and fell and hurt my knee quite *bad / badly*. I felt so *stupid / stupidly*! And I ran quite *slow / slowly* after that.

2 **Now look at the pictures 1–6 on sheet B. Put the texts above A–F in the correct order.**

Picture 1: ☐   Picture 3: ☐   Picture 5: ☐

Picture 2: ☐   Picture 4: ☐   Picture 6: ☐

3 **Look at the pictures 1–6 on sheet B again and complete the sentences with the correct adjective.**

> bad   black   curly   empty   fine   full   modern
> old   short   straight   tall   white

1 Paul's tracksuit is ....

2 Paul's hair is ....

3 The church is ....

4 The square at the start is ....

5 The 'bear' is ....

6 The weather is ....

A

Manchester United

Look at the pictures 1–6 on sheets A and B and read the texts about Manchester United.

- **Write the adjectives in their superlative form.**
  e.g. short ⇨ shortest, beautiful ⇨ most beautiful
- **Then complete each text with a sentence from the box.**

- His wife, Victoria, is the ex-Spice Girl, Posh Spice.
- He was British football's first superstar.
- Eight members of the team were killed in an air crash in Munich.
- Their football ground is called Old Trafford.
- They also won the European Cup.
- It was £29.1 million.

Manchester United

1

Manchester United is one of the (1 famous)

_____most famous_____ football clubs in the world.

They are perhaps the (2 popular)

_____ club in Britain and regularly

attract the (3 big) _____ crowds.

_____

_____

The club's (4 bad) _____ disaster
was in 1958.

_____

_____

It was the (5 sad) _____ day in the
club's history.

2

B

3

The golden age of the club was in the 1960s, with some of the (6 good) .... players in England: Bobby Charlton, Dennis Law, George Best, etc. People say that George Best was the (7 fast) .... player in the country.

....

....

1999 was perhaps the (8 successful) .... year in the history of the club. Manchester United won the FA Cup and the League.

....

....

4

5

The (9 expensive) .... transfer in the history of the club was when United bought Rio Ferdinand from Leeds United in 2002. The transfer fee was the (10 high) .... ever in Britain.

....

....

One of United's (11 talented) .... players is David Beckham, who was captain of the England team in the 2002 World Cup. He's also one of the (12 rich) .... players in the country.

....

....

6

A Saturday in Brighton

A

1 What did Alison and her boyfriend Tim do last Saturday? Look at the pictures 1–6 on sheet B.
  • Complete the sentences. Every *second* letter in the clues will give you the missing words!
  • Then match the sentences A–F sentences to the pictures 1–6.

A (t) (t) (r) (o) (a) (o) (i) (k) (n)

At midday, we ....*took*........ the ....*train*.......... to Brighton.

Picture: [ ] (oy)

B t m o e w t n

On Saturday morning, we .... in ....

Picture: [ ] (ex-)

C a s l p o e n n e t

And before taking the train home, we .... some time
.... on the beach.

Picture: [ ] (nd)

D t s r p a o i r n t e s d

Then we .... in the .... centre.

Picture: [ ] (b)

E m h e a a d l

After the concert, I .... a .... with Tim in
our favourite restaurant.

Picture: [ ] (ie)

F p b l e a a y c e h d

In the afternoon, our favourite group .... in a concert
on the ....

Picture: [ ] (fr)

2 Saturday ended in disaster! Write the letters in the circles in the order of the
pictures and find out who Alison and Tim met on their way back to the station.

They met Alison's ....

1

2

3

4

5

6

Mystery activities!

A group of teenagers are on holiday in Wales. They do different activities every day. What have they been doing today? Look at the pictures 1–10 on sheet B. They show you the teenagers – but not their equipment!

- Find the ten activities in the wordsquare and circle them. They can be in these directions: ↓ → ↘ ↗

- The wordsquare contains four other activities. Circle them in a different colour and write the four things Arthur has done.

1   Lauren has been ....

2   Tim and Matthew have been ....

3   Iqbal has ....

4   Kirsty ....

5   Cherie and Ellie ....

6   Danny ....

7   Nicky ....

8   Ben .... (on an artificial slope!).

9   Chloe and Emily ....

10 Nathalie ....

11 And Arthur? He's been very active! He .... ,
.... , and ....

S	K	I	I	N	G	R	O	W	I	N	G	A	W
Q	A	D	A	F	C	H	I	A	C	N	K	L	L
A	C	Y	C	L	I	N	G	T	I	Z	D	S	E
S	W	A	M	M	E	R	S	E	C	R	A	U	R
C	O	H	O	R	S	E	–	R	I	D	I	N	G
D	A	M	B	I	I	N	G	–	Z	E	S	B	S
C	A	N	O	E	I	N	G	S	E	S	H	A	O
L	P	N	A	E	I	S	H	K	D	I	B	T	O
I	D	W	C	H	T	H	A	I	B	N	O	H	I
M	O	R	S	I	I	M	M	I	N	G	A	I	N
B	H	I	K	I	N	G	X	N	L	J	I	N	G
I	F	N	I	N	G	G	E	G	F	I	N	G	U
N	E	G	C	K	S	W	I	M	M	I	N	G	A
G	Q	I	C	E	–	S	K	A	T	I	N	G	E

1

Lauren

2

Tim and Matthew

3

Iqbal

4

Kirsty

5

Cherie and Ellie

6

Danny

7

Nicky

8

Ben

9

Chloe and Emily

10

Nathalie

Are you a good detective?

1   **Look at the picture of Tom's room on sheet B. Can you find clues in the picture which show you what Tom has done today? Write ten things.**

1   Tom *has written a letter.* ....

2   He has ....

3   He ....

4   And I think he ....

5   He ....

6   I'm sure he ....

7   He ....

8   And perhaps he ....

9   I think he ....

10   And maybe he ....

2   **Cross out the verbs that don't make sense!**

1   I've just   (~~played~~   eaten   bought   had   ~~drunk~~)   a cake.

2   Karen has never   (been to   visited   taken   phoned   read)   Japan.

3   Have you ever   (hired   met   come   bought   seen)   a Charlie Chaplin film?

4   We've   (made   been   lived   worked   thought)   here for about ten years.

5   I'm sure they haven't   (gone out   come back   sent   returned   looked for)   yet.

Are you a good detective?

Johnny Depp

Complete the short biography of Johnny Depp with verbs from the box.
Use the past simple.

begin   get   go   have   leave   like   move   not last   play   want

A short biography of Johnny Depp

When Johnny Depp

(1) .... school, he

(2) .... in a band

called *The Kids*. But Johnny

(3) .... to act in

films, so he (4) ....

to Hollywood. First he

(5) .... a job as a

salesman but soon he

(6) .... to act in

films like *Platoon*, *Edward Scissorhands*

and *Nick of Time*.

Johnny (7) ....

several girlfriends while he was in

Hollywood but the relationships

(8) .... Although

he was an incredibly successful

actor, Johnny never really

(9) .... Hollywood. In 1998 he (10) .... to

France. He lives with his partner, Vanessa Paradis, and the couple have two children.

Britney Spears

1. Look at the interview with **Britney Spears** below. Read Britney's answers. Can you write the interviewer's questions?

An interview with
Britney Spears

Interviewer	(1) When .... ?
Britney	I was born on 2nd December 1981.
Interviewer	(2) .... ?
Britney	I lived in a little town in Louisiana until I was eleven.
Interviewer	(3) .... ?
Britney	I first performed in church choirs in my home town.
Interviewer	(4) .... ?
Britney	No, I didn't like school at all.
Interviewer	(5) .... ?
Britney	I worked on the Mickey Mouse Club from 1992 to 1993.
Interviewer	(6) .... ?
Britney	My first hit single came out in 1999. It was *Baby One More Time*.
Interviewer	(7) .... ?
Britney	I won the MTV Europe awards in 1999: Best Female, Best Pop, Best Breakthrough Artist and Best Song.

2. Now write one more question that you would like to ask Britney.

....
.... ?

The Titanic

Read the story of the Titanic.
- In texts 1 and 2, write the past participles of the verbs.
- In texts 3 and 4, write the passive of the verbs.
- In texts 5 and 6, change the active sentences to passive sentences.

1 The Titanic was (1 build) .... *built* ....

in 1911 in Belfast, Northern Ireland. The

ship was enormous and was (2 equip)

.... with some of the most

modern safety features of the age. In fact,

it was (3 think) .... that the

Titanic was unsinkable.

On her first journey, in April 1912,

passengers were (4 take) ....

on at Southampton (England), Cherbourg

(France) and Cork (Ireland). Life in the

first class was luxurious: evenings were

(5 spend) .... in the

restaurant or listening to concerts.

2

3 At 10 pm on Sunday 14th April, the Titanic

(6 warn) .... *was warned* .... about

icebergs in the area. But the Titanic

continued to travel at high speed and an

iceberg (7 hit) .... at

11.45 pm. Many passengers (8 wake)

.... by the shock.

4 All the crew (9 call) ....
onto the deck. The Titanic had sixteen
lifeboats and four rafts – enough only for
1200 people. The lifeboats (10 put)
.... into the sea but many
of them (11 not fill) ....
Many people still felt safer on board the
Titanic!

(12 The band played music until the boat
sank.) Music _was played until the boat sank_ .
(13 The Titanic sent SOS signals.)
SOS signals ....
....
(14 Five other ships received the signals.)
....
....

5

6 (15 The Carpathia rescued 705 people.)
....
....
(16 The crew gave them hot drinks and dry
clothes.)
....
....
(17 But 1522 people lost their lives that night.)
....
....

A

Murder in the flats

1 At 7 pm last night, there was a murder on the fourth floor of a block of flats. The police interviewed six witnesses.
  - **Complete the witnesses' statements. Write the verbs in the past continuous.**
  - **But are the witnesses reliable? Look at the picture on sheet B and correct any wrong information.**

I (iron, drink)

Miss Tibbs: When I heard the gunshot upstairs, I .... *was ironing* .... some ~~towels~~ *shirts*

and .... ~~a cup of tea~~ *a can of coke*.

2 (do, begin)

Tony: What .... we .... at 7 pm? Well, I don't

really remember. I think my parents .... the washing up

and I .... to play a computer game.

3 (tune)

Mr Mackay: No, I didn't hear anything. You see, I'm a musician and I

.... my guitar when it happened.

4 (read, pack)

Mrs O'Leary: Oh, I'm not sure. I think I .... a book on the sofa

and I think my children .... their bags for school.

But I could be wrong!

5 (have, serve)

Mr Watkins: Well, we .... our evening meal. In fact, my wife

.... the soup when we heard the noise from

upstairs.

6 (watch, do)

Mrs Atkins: I don't think I can help you. I was very tired yesterday evening. I

.... TV and Sophie (that's my daughter)

.... her homework, I think.

2 **Who is the most reliable witness?**

The most reliable witness is ....

A

Accidents waiting to happen

....

1   **Look at the picture on sheet B. Can you see what is going to happen?
Use the table to complete the sentences 1–10.**

X	is / are	going to		
			walk	his ladder.
			fall down	on a banana skin.
			slip	a manhole.
			crash	their ball.
			drop	wet.
			fall off	into each other.
			steal	their cakes.
			be	her purse.
			get	into a lamp post.
			lose	sick.

I   The girl who is waving ....

2   The man behind the old lady ....

3   The two bikes ....

4   The boy outside the burger bar ....

5   The delivery men ....

6   The window cleaner ....

7   The boy under the ladder ....

8   The boy who is coming out of the shop ....

9   The woman with the mobile phone ....

10   The two girls ....

2   **Look at the picture again. Can you see two other accidents that are going to
happen?**

Accident I   ....
....
....

Accident 2   ....
....
....

Jennifer Lopez

1 Jennifer Lopez is one of the most popular and successful film and music stars in the world. Look at the pictures and read the texts.
- In the first sentence of each text, cross out the wrong word.
- In the second sentence of each text, write the correct word from the box below. You'll only need five of the eight words in the box!

ate   ~~dancing~~   difficult   hair   hit   married   months   nose

1   When she was a girl, Jennifer Lopez lived

in a | poor / ~~rich~~ | flat in New York.

There was lots of music and

.... *dancing* .... in the home.

2   When Jennifer was a teenager, she and

her mother were in a | plane / car |

crash. Jennifer broke her ....

But today, she is one of the most beautiful

women in the world.

3   After she left school, Jennifer went to dance

classes: she always took the number six

| bus / train. | Later, her first album was

called *On the 6*, and it was a big

....

4 One day in 1997, Jennifer was in a restaurant. She fell in love with a Cuban | waiter / singer | called Ojani Noa. Jennifer .... Ojani in February 1997 but the marriage didn't last.

5 Jennifer married a second time in 2001: she married Cris Judd in a big | cave / tent | in the country near Los Angeles. But the marriage ended after only nine .... Will she marry again?

---

② **What about the future? Tick (✓) the sentences you agree with.**

1   I think Jennifer Lopez will have lots more hits. ☐

2   I think she will have no more hits. ☐

3   In my opinion, her film career is finished. ☐

4   In my opinion, she'll make many more great films. ☐

5   I think that she'll have children one day. ☐

6   I don't think she'll get married again. ☐

7   People will probably soon forget her name. ☐

8   She'll be a famous star for many years to come. ☐

A

Princess Diana

Read the story of Princess Diana. Complete each blank with one word that fits.

Diana Spencer was born (1) ...._on_............ 1st July 1961. She was often unhappy as a child: her mother left (2) .... father for another man when Diana was only six. And Diana never did very well (3) .... school. When she left school, she shared a flat in London (4) .... three good friends. She worked in a kindergarten.

(5) .... 1980, newspaper reporters often saw Diana near Prince Charles. 'Are they in love?' the newspapers (6) .... The answer was soon public news, and Prince Charles and Princess Diana married in St Paul's Cathedral in London on 29th July 1981. It (7) .... a fairy-tale wedding.

Diana's first child, William, was born in June 1982. Their (8) .... son, Harry, was born in September 1984. Diana tried (9) .... be a good mother but it wasn't easy with official visits to countries like Australia and New Zealand. In fact, Diana found life as (10) .... princess very difficult and was often unhappy.

B

Diana (11) .... happier when she talked with ordinary people. She visited hospitals and talked with children (12) .... people with AIDS. And she helped many charities. When Diana sold nearly of her eighty dresses in 1997, (13) .... gave the money to charities.

A photo of Diana, alone, in (14) .... of the Taj Mahal, on a tour of India in 1992, told the world (15) .... the problems in Diana's marriage. In the end, Charles and Diana separated. (16) .... divorced in February 1996. (17) .... was a very lonely time for Diana.

In August 1997, Diana was in Paris with her new boyfriend, Dodi Fayed. After dinner at the Ritz Hotel, Diana and Dodi drove away in (18) .... car. Reporters (19) .... photographers followed them. Then, in a tunnel, Diana's car crashed – and Diana was dead. In the next few days, people laid mountains of flowers outside Buckingham Palace – and in cities all (20) .... the world – to show their love for Diana.

A school trip

Last month, Class 9P went on a trip to Stratford-upon-Avon, the town where William Shakespeare was born. Lots of things went wrong – but the class still had a great time!
Look at the photos A–E of the trip on sheet B and then read the texts below.

- Write the letter of the right photo in the space below.
- Write texts 1, 3 and 5 using the words given. Write full sentences.
- Write good captions for the photos that do not have any (photos A and D).

1 coach – leave – late – Emily – eat – too many sweets – sick *The coach left late. Emily*	Photo: ....

2 When we got out of the coach in Stratford, Mr Kettle dropped his keys – and they fell down a drain in the road! We helped him to get the keys out again.	Photo: ....

3 after lunch – we – go rowing – river – Steve and Patrick – fall – water – laugh	Photo: ....

4 We went shopping in Stratford city centre. But Kevin White got lost: we looked for him everywhere, and we finally found him at the police station!	Photo: ....

5 visit – Shakespeare's house – when come out – bus not there – wait – two hours	Photo: ....

Our day in Stratford-upon-Avon

AH! STEVE AND PATRICK ARE HAVING A BATH – AT LAST!

WE'RE HERE – BUT WHERE'S THE BUS?

WHAT DID MUM SAY ABOUT TOO MANY SWEETS IN THE COACH?

Karen's visit to Britain

Karen from Kansas is on holiday in Britain. Her mother wanted her to visit all the cultural and historical places. In her letter home, Karen didn't tell her mother what she really did! Look at the map on sheet B. Then write what Karen really did.

Hi, Mom!

[1] I've been doing lots of active and cultural things here in Britain! I started in London, where I spent a whole afternoon in the British Museum. It was really interesting.

[2] Then I took a coach to Oxford. I was lucky: I had a lovely sunny day there, perfect for a tour of the old university buildings.

[3] After that, I took the train to Birmingham, where there's a really good Museum of Science and Industry.

[4] In York I stayed in the Youth Hostel, which was full of Americans! I visited the National Railway Museum with a group from the hostel: it was good fun.

[5] At the hostel, I met a boy from Durham, and he drove me there in his car. He showed me round the beautiful, ancient cathedral.

[6] And finally, I visited Edinburgh, which is a great place – full of life. I really liked Edinburgh Castle with the Scottish Crown Jewels. Britain is great!

See you soon,

Karen

[1] Karen didn't go to the British Museum. She went on the London Eye. After that, she went on a boat trip to Greenwich.

[2] ....
....
....

[3] ....
....
....

[4] ....
....
....

[5] ....
....
....

[6] ....
....
....

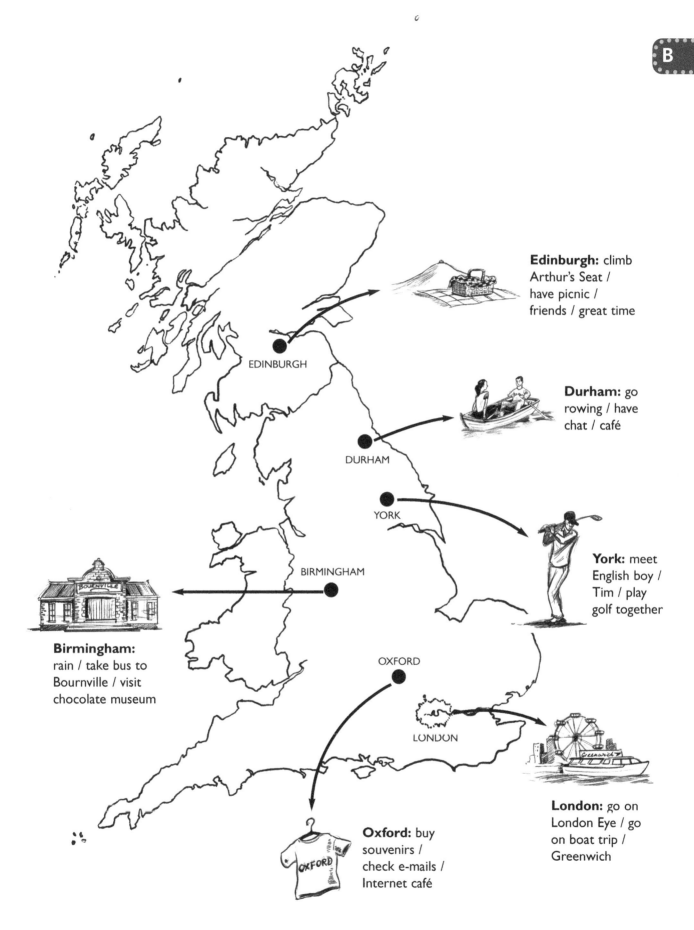

Edinburgh: climb Arthur's Seat / have picnic / friends / great time

Durham: go rowing / have chat / café

York: meet English boy / Tim / play golf together

Birmingham: rain / take bus to Bournville / visit chocolate museum

Oxford: buy souvenirs / check e-mails / Internet café

London: go on London Eye / go on boat trip / Greenwich

EDINBURGH

DURHAM

YORK

BIRMINGHAM

OXFORD

LONDON

A

Joe and Rachel

Rachel and Joe are boyfriend and girlfriend – but they have a stormy relationship. Look at the pictures on sheets A and B. Imagine what Rachel, Joe and Rachel's father say in the different scenes.

Joe: That was a good shot. You got a strike!

Rachel: Thanks.

Joe: Do you come bowling often?

Rachel: Yes, I (1) _do_ _____ .

Joe: Hey, what are you doing on Friday?

Rachel: (2) _____

_____

Joe: (3) _____

_____

Saturday 10th March, 6 pm.

Father: Where on earth have you been? It's eleven o'clock!

Rachel: (4) _____

_____

Father: (5) _____

_____ ?

Rachel: Joe.

Father: You're grounded* for a week! Now go to bed!

Rachel: (6) _____

_____

*grounded: have to stay at home

Friday 16th March, 11 pm

B

Saturday 24th March

Rachel: I saw you with a girl in town this morning! Who was she?

Joe: (7) ....

Rachel: I don't believe you! It's all over, Joe! I'm leaving you!

Joe: Rachel! (8) ....

....

Rachel: Well ...

Joe: And (9) ....

....

Rachel: Well, OK, Joe. Let's forget about it.

Joe: Sorry I'm late, Rachel.

Rachel: You're always late! What's your excuse this time?

Joe: (10) ....

....

Rachel: (11) ....

....

Joe: (12) ....

....

Saturday 31st March

How will the story end? Write your own ending.

....

....

....

....

....

....

A

The man with no memory

You are a police officer working in Selby. On the evening of 20th March, a man walks into the police station. He has no identification on him. And he can't answer your questions because he has lost his memory!

- **Look at sheet B: it shows you what the man has in his pockets.**
- **Try to work out as much as possible about the man from this evidence.**
- **Write your opinions on the form below.**

SELBY POLICE STATION

INCIDENT FORM X D S 1 2 9 4

<u>Details of the incident</u>

A man aged about forty came to the police station at 2100 hrs. He had lost his memory and had no identification on him.

This morning he went to the chemist's and bought ....

....

....

....

....

....

Clues from items found on the person
1 What did the person probably do in the hours before he lost his memory?

....

....

....

....

2 What can you say about his personal life, e.g. Is he single? Has he got a family?

....

....

3 Can you say anything about the person's health, aches, medical problems, etc?

....

....

4 Any other information?

....

....

....

....

B

Useful phrases

I think he might be/have a ...
I think he is probably ...
He probably has a ...
He probably went to ...

La Bella Italian restaurant
171 Doncaster Road, Selby

Lunchtime special deal

1 vegetarian lasagne	£4.50
1 glass red wine	£1.25
Total	**£5.75**

Service at 15% included
20th March
12.09 am

Merrydown Chemist

20 tablets aspirin	
Doro sun cream 2.5 dl	2.59
	3.49
Total	
	6.08

Received with thanks
20 – 03 –

Odeon cinemas
Screen 3
20th March   15.25

Harry Potter and the Chamber of Secrets

1 child ....£ 3 00

Odeon cinemas
Screen 3
20th March   15.25

Harry Potter and the Chamber of Secrets ....£ 4 00

1 adult..................................

Pennycutter Supermarkets
Kingston Road

Item	
1 x 500g Kittenkiddy cat food	99p
	99p
Total	100p
Received	
Change	1p
17.05 20 – 03 –	

Thank you for your custom

Penn Road Petrol Station, Selby

Pump	Product	Price	Qty	Value (£)
3	Unleaded	0.759	49.42	37.51
KitKat	Multipack	1.15	1	1. 15
			Total	**38. 66**

Cash Payment
Date 20th March 11.10am
Cashier ID 17   Rosie

Sarah, the scarf and the star

Sarah's big day was when the famous rock star, Tina Timpson, came into the café where she was working. Look at the pictures 1–6 on sheets **A** and **B**. Write two sentences for each picture. Use the past simple.

1

Last Monday morning ....

....

....

....

....

....

....

....

....

....

....

....

2

3

....

....

....

....

....

Nathalie's party

Look at the picture and tick the things you can see in it. The correct number
of ticks will give you Nathalie's age. Write Nathalie's age on the card!

an armchair	◯	a newspaper	◯
a bookcase	◯	a piano	◯
a bowl of fruit	◯	a picture	◯
cake	◯	a present	◯
cards	◯	a shelf	◯
a CD player	◯	a sofa	◯
a clock	◯	a tennis racquet	◯
a door	◯	a TV set	◯
glasses	◯	an adult	◯
a jug	◯		
a mobile phone	◯		

© MARY GLASGOW, AN IMPRINT OF SCHOLASTIC UK LTD.

Camping in the Lake District

Look at the picture, then look at the puzzle below.
- In the puzzle, shade in the boxes with the things you can see in the picture.
- Your shading will reveal a hidden object in the puzzle. What is it?

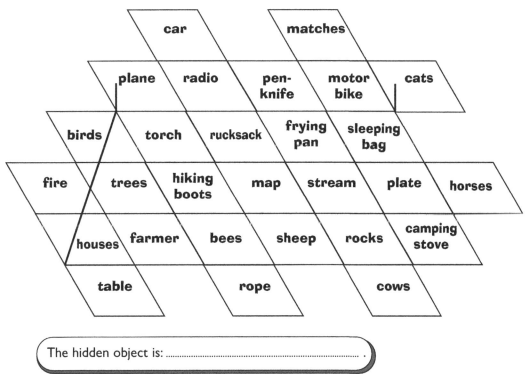

The hidden object is: ....

A

Famous places in Britain

Look at the photos on sheet B. Then look at the map and the descriptions below.
- **Match the descriptions 1–8 below to the photos A–H.**
- **Write the names of the places. Use the clues to help you!**

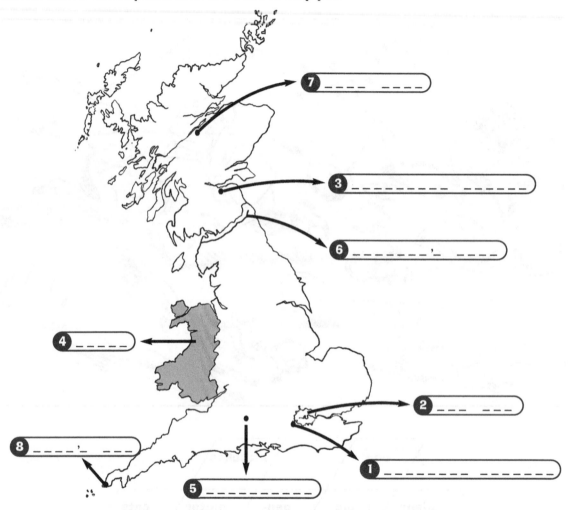

I This is Britain's biggest and busiest airport. It is just west of London. Picture ......*H*......

2 People think this is the name of the clock but really it's the name of the big bell. Picture ....

3 This is an old building and it stands on a rock in Scotland's capital city. Picture ....

4 This is in the west of Britain. Many people in this country speak two languages: English and their own Celtic language. Picture ....

5 This is a very famous monument. It was built five thousand years ago – a long time before the Romans came to Britain. Picture ....

6 The Romans built this to protect their land from people in the north. Picture ....

7 Does a monster live deep in the water in this place? Picture ....

8 This wild and rocky place is the furthest west in England. Picture ....

A DINEGHURB STLACE

B GESHENTONE

C GIB NEB

D HARIANDS LLAW

E HOLC SENS

F ABER
Gyrrwch yn ofalus
Please drive carefully
LESAW

G DANLS DEN

H WHARETHO PRAITOR

A

Famous places in the USA

(1) Here's a quiz on famous places in the USA. Read the clues. Then write the names of the places 1–10 in the right spaces on the map on sheet B. You may need to look in an atlas or on the Internet for this.

Quiz ? ? ? ? ?

1   This famous statue is in New York harbour. It was a present to the USA from France.

2   This city in the desert is world famous for its casinos and its night life.

3   This building in Washington DC is the home of the President of the United States.

4   These enormous waterfalls aren't the highest in the world – but they are really spectacular!

5   This is the longest river in North America.

6   This is where NASA sends astronauts into space.

7   This is the world's largest gorge: in places it is 1.5 km deep!

8   This is San Francisco's most famous bridge.

9   These enormous lakes are on the border between the USA and Canada. The largest is Lake Superior.

10   This park in the Rocky Mountains, Wyoming, is the USA's biggest National Park. Watch out for the grizzly bears!

(2) Can you find the names of two states hidden in the names on the map? Write the names below and colour in where the states are on the map. You can look in an atlas or on the Internet for help!

1   The letters in circles give you the name of a state famous for its oranges and alligators.

> The state is ....

2   Re-order the letters in squares to give you the name of a state famous for its wines, films and computers.

> The state is ....

B

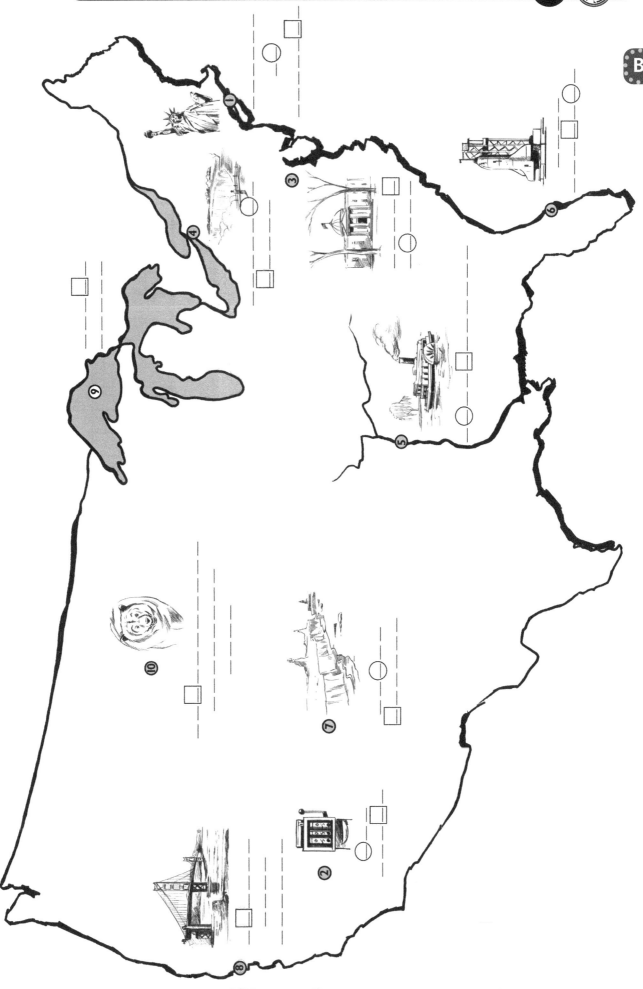

Travelling words

1 Look at the pictures and write the travel words in the puzzle.

2 Rearrange the letters in the grey squares to find how thousands of people travel in London.

They travel by ....

Food, glorious food

(1) **Can you find fifteen food words in the wordsquare? They can be in these directions: ↓ → ← ↘ ↗**

- **Tick the pictures when you find the words.**
- **One picture has no word in the wordsquare.**
  Which food is it? ....

E	G	R	A	P	E	F	R	U	I	T	C
A	C	R	N	E	K	C	I	H	C	O	H
P	O	T	A	T	O	E	S	B	H	C	O
D	I	E	N	P	H	A	S	O	E	R	C
R	A	S	P	B	E	R	R	I	E	S	O
A	J	E	S	T	U	S	Y	A	S	O	L
S	A	U	S	A	G	E	L	L	E	U	A
G	M	I	B	G	A	Q	C	D	U	S	T
O	R	A	E	G	O	U	A	H	A	A	E
S	T	R	A	W	B	E	R	R	I	E	S
P	R	C	H	E	R	R	I	E	S	P	E
Y	L	A	N	B	E	A	N	S	P	E	S

On the planet Mago

Life on the planet Mago is a bit like ours – but what is different?
Look at the picture and complete the sentences.

I   There are two .... in the sky.

2   The people have two .... on each side of their heads.

3   The dogs have six ....

4   The wheels of the .... are square.

5   The cars have don't have any ....

6   The .... is made of grass.

7   The houses all have round ....

8   The .... have two heads.

At the zoo

Look at the map of the zoo. The animals' names are mixed up.
Cross them out and write the correct names.

A   Recipe: Lemon meringue pie

1 Look at the picture and read the recipe. Find the correct words in the recipe and label the things in the picture.

1 ....rind.......

Recipe: Lemon Meringue Pie

250g shortcrust pastry	150g sugar
2 lemons	2 eggs
250ml cold water	40g butter
2 tablespoons of cornflour	

Roll out the pastry and put it into a 20cm round baking dish. Bake in the oven for 20–25 minutes.

Separate the egg yolks from the whites. Put the cornflour and 50g sugar into a bowl. Add a little of the water and mix into a paste.

Grate the lemons and put the grated rind into a pan with the rest of the water. Boil the water and rind, add the cornflour paste and mix well. Heat gently for one minute. Stir all the time. Remove from the heat.

Beat in the egg yolks, juice from the lemons and butter. Pour the mixture into the pastry case.

With an electric mixer, whisk the egg whites in a large bowl until stiff. Add 100g sugar little by little. Spoon the meringue over the lemon mixture. Bake in the oven for 40–45 minutes at 150°C.

(2) **Look at the pictures and find the verbs in the recipe.**
Write the verbs in the wordpath, in the same order as the pictures.

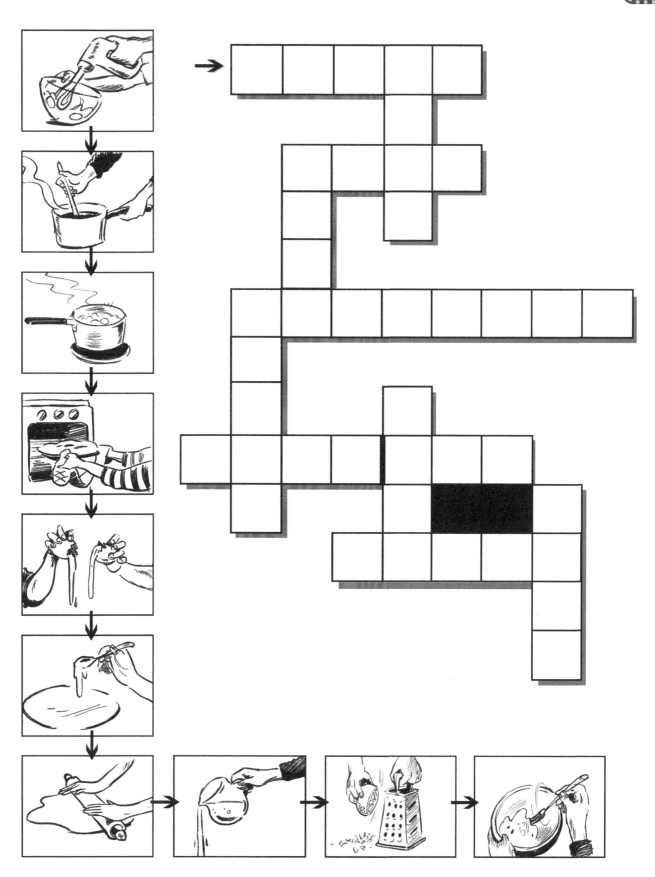

A

Josh's room

Look at the picture of Josh's room on sheet B. Some things in the picture have numbers – these are the clues for the crossword.

¹M	I	²R	R	O	R

IA = I across; ID = I down
19A = 19 across; 19D = 19 down
Numbers 2, 3, 4, 5 and 19A are all two words each.

A

Adverts you love and hate

1 Work with a partner.
Look at the adverts on sheet B. Discuss the points below. Do you always agree with each other?

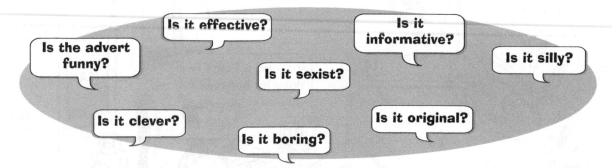

2 As a class, choose five adverts (from the TV, posters, radio, etc.).
Write the names of the products in the grid below.

Name of product	Opinion of advert								
	funny	effective	sexist	informative	silly	clever	boring	original	don't know the advert

3 Now do a survey in class.
- Ask your classmates what they think of the five adverts.
  What do you think of the advert for (name of the product)?
- Put small ticks (✓) in the appropriate boxes.
- When you have finished, look at the survey results. Does everyone have the same opinions about the five adverts?

B

The new ARK, by CDV

Room for all the family - and pets, too!

2.0 litre 100 kW EEC engine, electronic steering, halogen lamps, 6 airbags, triple sunroof

White-O Washing Powder

White-O Washing Powder with power

White-O

White-O

NEW

NEW

Housewives love it!

Paintballing fun

1. **Look at the picture of a paintballing game on sheet B.**
   - **What things can you hide behind, in the game?**
   - **Write the words in the puzzle.**

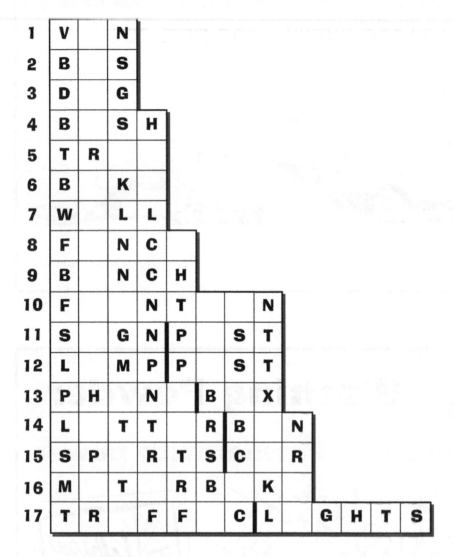

1	V		N									
2	B		S									
3	D		G									
4	B		S	H								
5	T	R										
6	B		K									
7	W		L	L								
8	F		N	C								
9	B		N	C	H							
10	F			N	T		N					
11	S		G	N	P		S	T				
12	L		M	P	P		S	T				
13	P	H		N		B		X				
14	L		T	T		R	B		N			
15	S	P		R	T	S	C		R			
16	M		T		R	B		K				
17	T	R		F	F		C	L		G	H	T	S

2. **Now play at paintballing! Work in pairs. Each student has a copy of the picture.**
   - **'Hide' five players – draw an X next to five things in the picture.**
   - **Take turns with your partner to 'fire a paintball', e.g.**

Student A

Someone is behind the sports car.

Student B

Yes, you're right. / No, you're wrong.

The first person to hit all five of his/her partner's players wins the game!

A

Spot the difference

Student A

Look at the picture of the concert.
Your partner's picture is *almost* the same – but there are ten differences! Describe your picture, one sentence at a time, e.g.
Student A: In my picture, the saxophonist has long hair.
Student B: Same here. In my picture, the guitarist ...

People in the group:
• guitarist
• singer
• drummer
• saxophonist

Student B

Look at the picture of the concert.
**Your partner's picture is _almost_ the same – but there are ten
differences! Describe your picture, one sentence at a time, e.g.**
Student A: In my picture, the saxophonist has long hair.
Student B: Same here. In my picture, the guitarist …

People in the group:
• guitarist
• singer
• drummer
• saxophonist

A day out in York

A

Student A

It's a Saturday in the summer holidays. You and your partner are in York for the day. You each have different information about things to do but you can't show your partner your information.

- **Discuss what there is to do, and choose activities for the *morning*, *afternoon* and *evening*.**
- **You each have £12 to spend. Check the prices and opening times.**

Ten Pin Bowling

Monday to Friday:	12pm until midnight
Saturday and Sunday:	10am until midnight
Game Prices:	
Adult:	£3.75 per person per game
Child:	£2.75 per child per game
Shoe Hire:	£1.00 per person

National Railway Museum

Visit the museum's large collection of over 100 trains, telling the history of the railway from Stephenson's Rocket to Eurostar.
Open daily 10.00–18.00

Admission: Free

Highfields
Sports Centre

Badminton courts	£4.50
Table tennis	£2.50

Open	Mon–Fri: 10.30am – 8.30pm
	Sat: 9.30am – 10.30pm

LaZer Nightclub

Open every night 8pm–2.30am
Entrance £3.50
Over 21's only

Clifford's Tower

Visit York's ruined castle
Opening times:
9.30am–7pm
Adults £2.10;
Children £1.10

Sunshine Cruises

Boat Trips on the River Ouse
Departure times:
10.30am, 12.00pm, 1.30pm, 3.00pm

Tickets: adult £6, child (6–15) £5.50

Trips last 1 hour

Student B

It's a Saturday in the summer holidays. You and your partner are in York for the day. You each have different information about things to do but you can't show your partner your information.

- Discuss what there is to do, and choose activities for the *morning*, *afternoon* and *evening*.
- You each have £12 to spend. Check the prices and opening times.

Jorvik Viking Centre

Travel back in time and a visit a Viking town. Look inside the houses, hear the children playing ... and smell all the smells!
Open daily 09:00–17:30
Adult: £6.95
Child (5–15): £5.10

Queen Mary's Stables

Horse-riding (afternoons only)
1 hour lesson £15
1 hour trek £12

Rex Cinema

Star Wars showing 3.45pm, 6.25pm, 9.05pm (£3.50)

If you're in York, why not visit **Fairfax House**?

In this 18th century house, you can see the beautiful rooms the family lived in – and visit the kitchens, where the servants worked. We loved it!

Monday to Thursday:
11.00am to 5.00pm

Saturday: 11.00am to 5.00pm

Sunday: 1.30pm to 5.00pm

Adults £4.50 Children £1.50

AquaWorld

Not just a swimming-pool - mega-waves, slides and jacuzzi!

Fun for all the family!

Adult: £3.50; Child (under 16) £2.50
Mon, Wed, Fri 16:00–20:00
Sat & Sun   10:00–17:00

Bytes Internet Café

Internet access for £1.90 per half hour;
£3.50 per hour and great coffee, too!

Spy-catcher

(1) Match the pieces of the jigsaw puzzle on the left with the pieces on the right to find the names of sixteen things you might find in an office. Tick the things you can see in the picture on sheet **B**.

plant ✓ ....

....

....

....

....

....

....

....

(2) Now play *Find the Bug!*
- **Work in pairs. Each student has a photocopy of the picture of the office on sheet B.**
- **Student A is a spy! He/She puts five bugs* in this office: he/she puts a cross in five of the circles in the picture.**
- **Student B asks questions to find out where the bugs are, e.g. *Is there a bug under the radiator?***
- **Student A can only answer: *Yes, there is* or *No, there isn't*.**
- **How many questions does it take Student B to find all five bugs?**
- **Now swap roles: Student B hides five bugs. Student A looks for them.**

> The student who finds the bug with the fewest questions wins the game!

* A bug is a tiny microphone which spies use to listen to conversations.

Key:

behind   under   on top of   in

A

Twenty questions

Student A

Your partner has a photo of a famous person. Ask questions to find out who it is.

* **Your partner can only answer *yes* or *no*.**
* **You can only ask twenty questions!**

Is it a man?

Is he/she a politician?

A famous event: the astronaut Neil Armstrong walks on the moon

Student B

Your partner has a photo of a famous event. Ask questions to find out what it is.

• Your partner can only answer *yes* or *no*.
• You can only ask twenty questions!

A famous person: Charles, Prince of Wales

A Test your powers of communication!

Student A

(1) Work in pairs.
- **Describe Picture A to your partner. Watch your partner draw and guide him/her, e.g.** *No, it's bigger than that. It's round, not square.*
- **When the drawing is finished, show your partner Picture A – how good is your partner's drawing?** *Very good? Quite good? Dreadful?*

Picture A

(2) Work in pairs.
- **Now your partner describes Picture B and you draw it.**
- **When you have finished, your partner will show you Picture B – how good is your drawing?** *Very good? Quite good? Dreadful?*

Picture B

Student B

1 Work in pairs.
- **Your partner describes Picture A and you draw it.**
- **When you have finished, your partner will show you Picture A – how good is your drawing? *Very good? Quite good? Dreadful?***

Picture A

2 Work in pairs.
- **Describe Picture B to your partner. Watch your partner draw and guide him/her, e.g. *No, it's bigger than that. It's further to the left.***
- **When the drawing is finished, show your partner Picture B – how good is your partner's drawing? *Very good? Quite good? Dreadful?***

Picture B

Football reporter

(1) **There was a dramatic football match last Saturday and you were the reporter. Complete your report. Use the past simple.**

1   The match ....*began*.......... badly. Robertson ....*fouled*.......... Jones in the penalty area – he ....*kicked*.......... him viciously in the foot. (begin, foul, kick) ☐

2   The referee .... the incident and .... Robertson off immediately. (see, send) ☐

3   Jackson .... the penalty kick. As he .... up to the ball, he .... to hesitate slightly. (take, run, seem) ☐

4   The crowd .... as Johnson, the Rovers', goalkeeper, ... a dramatic save. (roar, make) ☐

5   There .... a dramatic moment right at the end of the first half. United's Johnny James .... the ball to Black. (be, pass) ☐

6   Black .... , he .... aim – and .... (turn, take, score) ☐

7   Rovers .... to make the score one–all. MacDonald .... the ball towards the net but he .... to score. (try, head, fail) ☐

8   The game .... dramatically. The Rovers fans .... madly as Wilson .... the ball from 25 yards. But he .... the net. United .... the match, one–nil. (end, cheer, kick, miss, win) ☐

(2) **Look at pictures A–E on sheet B. Match the photos to five of the sections 1–8 above. Write the correct letters next to the right sections.**

(3) **Work in pairs.**
- **Cut out the five photos A–E on sheet B.**
- **Your partner shuffles them. You are the reporter!**
- **Pick up the pictures and say what happened in the match – in the order of the photos.**
- **Now swap roles: you shuffle and your partner reports.**

> You can use real teams if you like, or even invent super teams with famous players.

Useful expressions
- the crowd roared when ...
- there was a dramatic moment when...
- in the (89th) minute ...
- right at the beginning of the match ...
- just before the final whistle ...
- (three) minutes into the (first) half ...

A

B

C

D

E

Holiday postcards

1 **Read the sentences 1–12 below.**
* **The underlined words are in the wrong sentences. Cross them out and write the right word from another sentence.**
* **Match the sentences 1–12 to the postcards A–D on sheet B. Write the letter of the right postcard next to each sentence.**

1 I really like swimming but the sea is quite ~~heavy~~ *cold*! ☐

2 My ~~kitchens~~ are too tight and my feet hurt! ☐

3 Skiing isn't easy but it's great ~~palace~~. ☐

4 We visited this ~~fun~~ yesterday. ☐

5 There's plenty of snow here because it snowed ~~tomorrow~~. ☐

6 I'm going to try water-skiing ~~yesterday~~. ☐

7 I love hiking: we walk about twenty ~~gardens~~ a day. ☐

8 I like ~~enjoying~~ my book on the beach. ☐

9 Many of the rooms were boring but I liked going round the old ~~walking boots~~! ☐

10 I fall over ten times every day but I'm still ~~reading~~ it! ☐

11 We went rowing on the lake in the ~~miles~~. ☐

12 My rucksack is too ~~cold~~ *heavy*. ☐

2 **The postcards A–D on sheet B show different kinds of places to go to on holiday. What do you like doing on holiday? Complete the sentence.**

I prefer holidays in places like postcard .... because ....

....

A

B

C

D

Formula 1

1 What do you think of Formula 1?
Tick the words and phrases that describe Formula 1.

fast ☐	you can do it at home ☐
boring ☐	dangerous ☐
glamorous ☐	sweet ☐
delicious ☐	you need skill ☐
exciting ☐	wide ☐
quiet ☐	noisy ☐
comfortable ☐	bad for the environment ☐
expensive ☐	difficult ☐

2 Choose *four* words or phrases from Exercise 1 that best give your opinion.

....

....

Designer clothes

(1) **Are these opinions of designer clothes positive or negative?**
- **Draw a smile if the comment is positive.** ☺
- **Draw a frown if the comment is positive.** ☹

1 Designer clothes are much more stylish than boring, ordinary clothes. ⊙⊙

2 I think they're a complete waste of money! ⊙⊙

3 Designer clothes cost far too much – they're a rip-off! ⊙⊙

4 It's good to wear designer clothes because they're a bit different. ⊙⊙

5 I think designer clothes are better quality than other clothes. ⊙⊙

6 I don't think designer clothes are very good value. ⊙⊙

7 Designer clothes are really cool. ⊙⊙

8 People only wear designer clothes to show off how much money they have. ⊙⊙

(2) **Write *your* opinion about designer clothes.**

A

A school for wizards

1 You are going to write a book set in a wizard school. First you need to think about the people in the book. Here are some words to help you. Write them in the right word-web below.

a swot	old-fashioned
blond	plump
brave	putting spells on people
chocolate	straight
dragons	strict
~~friendly~~	tall
generous	telling jokes
giving homework	thin
good fun	trendy
lying in bed	turning people into
nasty	animals

friendly

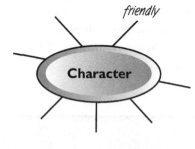

Character

Appearance and clothes

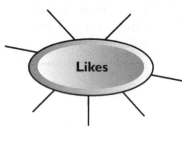

Likes

2 Look at the pictures of two teachers and two pupils at the school. Write a description of each person. Invent the details – use your imagination!

Name: ....

Age: ....

Appearance: *She has long curly dark hair. She* ....

Character: ....

Likes: ....

B

Name: ....

Age: ....

Appearance: ....
....

Character: ....
....

Likes: ....
....

Name: ....

Age: ....

Appearance: ....
....

Character: ....
....

Likes: ....
....

Name: ....

Age: ....

Appearance: ....
....

Character: ....
....

Likes: ....
....

(3) **Now decide what the people think of each other. Complete the sentences and then write some sentences of your own.**

.... is a good friend of .... because ....
....

.... hates .... because ....
....

....

A car for everyone

(1) **Look at the photos of the cars A–D on sheet B.**
Tick the statements which apply to each car.

		A Beetle	B Sports car	C People carrier	D Smart
1	It has a top speed of over 250 km/h.				
2	It has its engine in the back.				
3	There isn't room for four people.				
4	It has two doors.				
5	It has seven seats.				
6	It's very expensive.				
7	It doesn't use a lot of petrol.				
8	It's old-fashioned.				
9	It's modern.				
10	You can't pack a lot of luggage in it.				
11	It's very easy to park in small spaces in town.				
12	It goes from 0 to 100 km/h in 4.9 seconds.				
13	You can fold a seat and make it into a table.				
14	I really like this car.				
15	I would never buy a car like this.				

(2) **Which car do you think this person would buy?**

> James Reader is an artist. He's thirty-eight and likes stylish things – he lives in an old windmill. He doesn't want to drive fast. Image is important to him – he likes to be different! He likes old cars that have style.

James would probably buy a ....

(3) **Choose another car and describe someone who might buy it.**

Car: ....

....

....

....

....

....

....

a 1960's Beetle

a sports car

a people carrier

Smart, a small car for town driving

TV quotes

1 Match the speech bubbles 1–8 to the TV programmes A–H they came from.

A thriller
B weather forecast
C quiz show
D sports programme
E advert
F nature documentary
G music programme
H news

1 Congratulations – you've won £1 million! *C*

2 Straight in at Number 1 with her new single, it's Kylie Minogue!

3 Tomorrow it will be cold but sunny.

4 But first, the headlines. The Prime Minister has met the US President at the White House.

5 New *Shine* shampoo. It leaves your hair shiny and soft.

6 Shhh! Did you hear that noise? I think there's someone outside.

7 And the British team wins the 4x100m relay! Olympic gold for Britain!

8 This tiny animal lives in the sand of the Sahara desert. It sleeps during the day ...

2 Look at the TV sets on sheet B. TV set A is showing a romantic film and TV set B is showing an advert for chocolate. Write what you think the people are saying in the speech bubbles. Your answers can be serious or funny!

3 Which type of TV programme you really hate, and why?

I really hate .... because
....
....
....
....
....

Mystery boy

Look at the picture and answer the questions. Use your imagination!

1 Where is this happening? (which town? country?)

2 What has just happened?

3 What does the boy have under his jacket?

4 Where is he running to/ from?

5 How is the boy feeling?

6 What do you think is going to happen next?

7 How is the story going to end?

A strange story

Look at the pictures. You are going to invent a story using at least four of the pictures.
You get five points for every one of the pictures you manage to get into the story!
Write your story on a sheet of paper.

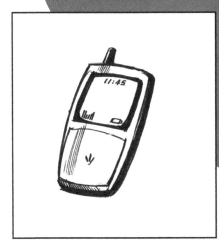

Reporting a bank robbery

1 Look at the pictures on sheet B and read the newspaper article about the bank robbery. Cross out any wrong information in the article and correct it.

The Gazette   6th April

Robbery at Smedley's Bank

£90,000 was stolen yesterday morning in a robbery at Smedley's Bank. A gang of *two* ~~three~~ bank robbers entered the bank armed with knives. Their faces were hidden by masks. Three customers were in the bank at the time: they were told to sit down and their hands were tied.

One of the bank's employees, Mrs Jones, was told to hand over the money from the till. She was then ordered to open the safe. The robbers' white van, driven by the fourth member of the gang, was waiting in the street outside.

The police were called and managed to track down the robbers to a farm. The farm was raided at midnight and two people were arrested: a man and a woman. Police dogs were used but nothing was found.

---

2 Imagine you were one of the people involved in the story, e.g. a police officer, a gang member, a member of the public, a bank employee. Write to a friend and say what happened and how you felt, e.g.
I was at work as usual, when suddenly ...
Can you write it without using any verbs in the passive? e.g.
The robbers told us to sit down.

....

....

....

....

....

....

....

....

London through the ages

(1) **Look at the pictures A–C on sheet B. Which pictures do the sentences 1–4 below describe: A, B or C?**

1 Women are freer to do and wear what they like, for example, women often wear trousers. ☐

2 London was the capital of a large empire and many grand buildings were built, for example Big Ben was only fifty years old. ☐

3 The Internet means that you can do many things without leaving your house, for example order food and have it delivered by van. ☐

4 Before the invention of the petrol and steam engines, the fastest way to travel was by horse. ☐

(2) **Compare the three ages. Complete the sentences.**

• **Transport**

A: In the Middle Ages, people walked or travelled on horseback.

B: In the late nineteenth century,

....

C: Today many families have two cars.

• **Shopping**

A: In the Middle Ages, people made the things they needed.

B: In the late nineteenth century,

....

C: Today ....

....

• **Entertainment**

A: In the Middle Ages, some travelling actors put on shows.

B: In the late nineteenth century, people went to the theatre or to music halls.

C: Today ....

....

• **Choose a topic: Communications/ Clothes/Buildings etc.**

A: In the Middle Ages, ...

....

B: In the late nineteenth century,

....

C: Today ....

....

(3) **What do you think?**

I think the .... were / was / is the best age to live in because

....

....

....

....

Answer Key

Pages 6–7
The fashion boutique

① **In Picture B ...**
1 there's a mirror on the wall.
2 there are some sweets (on the counter).
3 there isn't a lamp (in the corner).
4 there aren't any flowers (in the vase).
5 there's a curtain (in the cubicle/changing room).
6 there aren't any posters (on the wall).
7 there are some shoes (for sale).
8 there is a boy (outside the cublicle/changing room).
9 there isn't a bag (outside the cublicle/changing room).
10 there aren't any T-shirts (for sale).

②
Sharon bought a *blouse*.

③ (Suggested answers)
1 (hat), sock, skirt/shirt, jumper, (pyjamas), trousers
2 (skirts), shirts, shorts

Pages 8–9
The assault course

①
1 through; 2 from, to; 3 over; 4 under; 5 into, across;
6 along; 7 up, down; 8 between

②
a 2; b 5; c 3; d 1; e 4

③ (Students' own answer, e.g. I'm scared. /This is fun./
I don''t like this!)

Pages 10–11
A holiday in Devon

①
The correct order of photos is: I, C, E, D, F, G, A, B, H.
Saturday's activity is *mountain biking*.

② (Students' own answers)

③ (Students' own answers)

Pages 12–13
The fun run

①
A loudly, good
B warm, absolutely
C really happy, completely
D heavy, slow
E loud, amazingly
F badly, stupid, slowly

②
Picture 1: B
Picture 2: A
Picture 3: E
Picture 4: D
Picture 5: F
Picture 6: C

③
1 black; 2 curly; 3 old; 4 full; 5 tall; 6 fine

Pages 14–15
Manchester United

1 most famous; 2 most popular; 3 biggest;
4 worst; 5 saddest; 6 best; 7 fastest;
8 most successful; 9 most expensive;
10 highest; 11 most talented; 12 richest

Missing sentence for Text 1: Their football ground is called
Old Trafford.
Missing sentence for Text 2: Eight members of the team
were killed in an air crash in Munich.
Missing sentence for Text 3: He was British football's first
superstar.
Missing sentence for Text 4: They also won the European
Cup.
Missing sentence for Text 5: It was £29.1 million.
Missing sentence for Text 6: His wife, Victoria, is the ex-Spice
Girl, Posh Spice.

Pages 16–17
A Saturday in Brighton

①
1 took, train
2 met, town
3 spent, alone
4 trained, sports
5 had, meal
6 played, beach

②
A 3; B 1; C 6; D 2; E 5; F 4
They met Alison's *ex-boyfriend*.

Pages 18–19
Mystery activities!

1 Lauren has been water-skiing.
2 Tim and Matthew have been rowing.
3 Iqbal has been canoeing.
4 Kirsty hasn been dancing.
5 Cherie and Ellie have been hiking.
6 Danny has been fishing.
7 Nicky has been ice-skating.
8 Ben has been skiing (on an artificial slope).
9 Chloe and Emily have been sunbathing.
10 Nathalie has been horse-riding.
11 And Arthur? He's been very active! He has been sailing,
cycling, swimming and climbing.

Pages 20–21
Are you a good detective?

① (Any ten of:)
he has been hiking
he has been swimming
he has read a (car) magazine
he has bought a ticket for a concert
he has played football
he has written a letter
he has played the guitar
he has made a model car
he has eaten an apple
he has drunk some coke
he has played cards
he has had a shower/bath

② Students cross out:
1 played, drunk
2 taken, read
3 met, come
4 made, thought
5 sent, looked for

Page 22
Johnny Depp

1 left; 2 played; 3 wanted; 4 went/moved; 5 got; 6 began;
7 didn't last; 8 liked; 9 moved/went

Page 23
Britney Spears

① (Suggested answers)
1 When were you born?
2 Where did you live when you were a little girl?
3 Where did you first perform?
4 Did you like school?
5 How long did you work on the Mickey Mouse
   Club?/Where did you work when you left school?/ When
   did you work on the Mickey Mouse Club?
6 When did your first hit single come out?/What happened
   in 1999?
7 What happened then?/Did anything else happen
   that year?

② (Students' own question)

Pages 24–25
The Titanic

1 built
2 equipped
3 thought
4 taken
5 spent
6 was warned
7 was hit
8 were woken
9 were called
10 were put
11 were not filled
12 Music was played (by the band) until the boat sank.
13 SOS signals were sent (by the Titanic).
14 The signals were received by five other ships.
15 705 people were rescued by the Carpathia.
16 They were given hot drinks and dry clothes (by the
   crew).
17 But 1522 lives were lost that night.

Pages 26–27
Murder in the flats

①
1 When I heard the gunshot upstairs, I *was ironing* some
   shirts and *drinking* a can of coke.
2 What *were we doing* at 7 pm? Well, I don't really
   remember. I think my parents (*were doing* the washing up)
   were arguing/fighting and I (*was beginning* to play a
   computer game) was listening to (some) CDs/music.
3 No, I didn't hear anything. You see, I'm a musician and I
   (*was tuning* my guitar) was talking on the phone when it
   happened.
4 Oh, I'm not sure. I think I *was reading* a book on the sofa
   and I think my children *were packing* their bags for school.
   But I could be wrong!
5 Well, we *were having* our evening meal. In fact, my wife *was
   serving* the fish when we heard the noise from upstairs.
6 I don't think I can help you. I was very tired yesterday
   evening: I (*was watching* TV) was sleeping (in front of the
   TV set), and Sophie (that's my daughter) (*was doing* her
   homework) was playing her violin, I think.

②
The most reliable witness is *Mrs O'Leary.*

Pages 28–29
Accidents waiting to happen

Note to the teacher:
Give key words to prompt students if necessary.

① (Suggested answers)
1 The girl who is waving is going to fall down a a
   manhole.
2 The man behind the old lady is going to steal her purse.
3 The two bikes are going to crash into each other.
4 The boy outside the burger bar is going to be sick.
5 The delivery men are going to drop their cakes.
6 The window cleaner is going to fall off his ladder.
7 The boy under the ladder is going to get wet.
8 The boy who is coming out of the shop is going to slip
   on a banana skin.
9 The woman with the mobile phone is going to walk into
   a lamp post.
10 The girls who are playing tennis are going to lose their
   ball.

② (Sample answers)
The woman who is running for her bus is going to miss it.
The football is going to break a window.

Pages 30–31
Jennifer Lopez

①
1 poor, dancing
2 car, nose
3 train, hit
4 waiter, married
5 tent, months

② (Students' own answers)

Pages 32–33
Princess Diana

(Suggested answers)
1 on; 2 her; 3 at; 4 with; 5 In; 6 asked; 7 was; 8 second;
9 to; 10 a; 11 was; 12 and; 13 she; 14 front;
15 about; 16 They; 17 It; 18 a/their; 19 and; 20 over

Pages 34–35
A school trip

① (Suggested answers)
1 The coach left late. Emily ate too many sweets in the
  coach and was very sick.
  Photo: E
2 Photo: D
3 After lunch we went rowing on the river. Steve and
  Patrick fell into the water. We all laughed!
  Photo : B
4 Photo: A
5 We visited Shakespeare's house in Stratford. But when we
  came out, the bus wasn't there. We had to wait two hours
  for the bus!
  Photo: C

Possible captions for Photo B: We rescue Kevin from the
police./Why is Kevin at the police station?!
Possible captions for Photo D: Mr Kettle looking for gold in
Stratford./What is Mr Kettle doing?

Pages 36–37
Karen's visit to Britain

Notes:
Greenwich: Greenwich is a suburb of London. The line of
0° longitude passes through it. There is a big naval museum
and you can go aboard an old sailing ship there (called the
Cutty Sark).

Bourneville: Bourneville is a suburb of Birmingham, where
the Cadbury's chocolate factory is situated. Cadbury World
is a big tourist attraction. Cadbury's also make a bar of
chocolate called Bourneville.

Arthur's Seat: Arthur's Seat is a hill in the very centre of
Edinburgh. There are fine views of the city from the top.

(Suggested answers)
Paragraph 1: Karen didn't go to the British Museum. She
went on the London Eye. After that, she went on a boat trip
to Greenwich.

Paragraph 2: She didn't go on a tour of the university. She
bought some souvenirs and checked her e-mails in an
Internet café.

Paragraph 3: She didn't go to the Museum of Science and
Industry. It was raining and she took the bus to Bournville
and visited the chocolate museum.

Paragraph 4: She didn't visit the National Railway Museum.
She met an English boy called Tim and they played golf
together.

Paragraph 5: They didn't visit the cathedral. They went
rowing and then they had a chat in a café.

Paragraph 6: She didn't visit Edinburgh Castle. She climbed
Arthur's Seat and had a picnic with some friends and had a
great time.

Pages 38–39
Joe and Rachel

(Sample answers)

Rachel: (2) Why do you ask? / Why are you asking?
Joe: (3) Would you like to come bowling with me? At
six, say?

Father: Where on earth have you been? It's eleven
o'clock!
Rachel: (4) I've been bowling. I'm sorry, Dad. I didn't see
what the time was.
Father: (5) You've been with that boy again, haven't you?
What's his name?
Rachel: Joe.
Father: You're grounded for a week! Now go to bed!
Rachel: (6) But that's not fair, Dad!

Rachel: I saw you with a girl in town this morning! Who
was she?
Joe: (7) Oh, only the girl who lives next door.
Rachel: I don't believe you! It's all over, Joe! I'm leaving
you!
Joe: Rachel! (8) I promise you: I love you, and only you!
Rachel: Well...
Joe: And (9) I'd like to invite you to the Oasis concert
on Saturday.
Rachel: Well, OK, Joe. Let's forget about it.

Joe: Sorry I'm late, Rachel.
Rachel: You're always late! What's your excuse this time?
Joe: (10) I missed the bus/The bus broke down.
Rachel: (11) I don't believe you. And I'm getting fed up
with always waiting for you, Joe.
Joe: (12) Well, I'm getting fed up with you always
moaning.

(Students' own ending for the story)

Pages 40–41
The man with no memory

(Sample answers)
1 This morning he went to the chemist's and bought
  twenty tablets of aspirin and some sun cream. Then he
  bought some petrol at Penn Road Petrol Station. He had
  lunch at La Bella Italian restaurant. In the afternoon he
  bought some cat food at Pennycutter Supermarket in
  Kingston Road and then he went to the cinema to see
  'Harry Potter and the Chamber of Secrets'.

2 I think he might have a wife or girlfriend: he had a photo
  of a woman in his pocket. He probably has a child
  because he bought a child's ticket as well as an adult
  ticket for the cinema.

3 He bought aspirin: did he feel unwell? I think he might
  have pale or sensitive skin: he bought sun cream in
  March. He ordered a vegetarian lasagne: is he perhaps
  vegetarian?

4 He bought petrol and he had car keys in his pocket, so
  he probably has a car. I think he might be a customer or
  employee of the Yorkshire Bank, because he had a
  Yorkshire Bank pen in his pocket. And he probably has a
  cat as he bought cat food at the supermarket.

Pages 42–43
Sarah, the scarf and the star

(Sample answers)
1 Last Monday morning Sarah left her home at 7.55 am to go to her job. Her mother gave her a scarf because it was cold.
2 Sarah was working in the café when the famous star Tina Timpson came in. Tina was wearing a glamorous dress and she was with a young man in dark glasses.
3 Sarah was thrilled but when she brought the red wine that Tina had ordered, she accidentally spilt some wine over Tina's dress. Tina was very annoyed.
4 But Sarah had a brilliant idea. She put her mother's scarf over Tina's shoulders. You couldn't see the wine stain any more and Tina was happy again.
5 When Sarah arrived home that evening, she wanted to tell her mother about Tina. But her mother was angry because Sarah had not brought back her scarf.
6 Later that evening, when Sarah and her mother were watching the news, they saw Tina Timpson on TV – and she was wearing Sarah's mother's scarf! Now Sarah's mother was delighted too!

Page 44
Nathalie's party

Students tick the following:
a cake, cards, a CD player, a clock, a door, glasses, a jug, a mobile phone, a picture, a present, a shelf, a sofa, a tennis racquet

Nathalie is 13 years old today.

Page 45
Camping in the Lake District

The things in the picture are:
bees, a camping stove, a frying pan, a map, a plate, a rucksack, sheep (plural), a sleeping bag, a stream, a torch, rocks, walking boots

The hidden object is a *tent*.

Pages 46–47
Famous places in Britain

1 Heathrow Airport H
2 Big Ben C
3 Edinburgh Castle A
4 Wales F
5 Stonehenge B
6 Hadrian's Wall D
7 Loch Ness E
8 Land's End G

Pages 48–49
Famous places in the USA

①
1 Statue of Liberty
2 Las Vegas
3 White House
4 Niagara Falls
5 Mississippi
6 Cape Kennedy
7 Grand Canyon
8 Golden Gate
9 Great Lakes
10 Yellowstone National Park

1 Florida; 2 California

Page 50
Travelling words

1 ticket
2 coach
3 motorway
4 roundabout
5 bus
6 plane
7 ferry
8 garage
9 car
10 train
11 bridge
12 airport
13 bike

Many people in London travel by *Underground*.

Page 51
Food, glorious food

The words in the wordsquare are:
beans, bread, cheese, cherries, chicken, chips, chocolates, eggs, grapefruit, grapes, jam, potatoes, raspberries, sausage, strawberries

The picture with no word in the wordsquare is *apples*.

Page 52
On the planet Mago

1 suns; 2 ears; 3 legs; 4 cars; 5 doors; 6 road; 7 windows; 8 birds

Page 53
At the zoo

~~kangaroo~~ elephant
~~giraffe~~ kangaroo
~~camel~~ penguin
~~crocodile~~ wolf
~~monkey~~ giraffe
~~bear~~ sealion

~~tiger~~ monkey
~~elephant~~ lion
~~sealion~~ crocodile
~~penguin~~ bear
~~lion~~ gorilla
~~gorilla~~ camel

Pages 54–55
Recipe: Lemon meringue pie

①
1 rind; 2 lemons; 3 cornflour; 4 water; 5 bowl; 6 spoon; 7 mixer; 8 eggs; 9 baking dish; 10 sugar; 11 pastry

②
whisk, stir, boil, bake, separate, spoon, roll out, pour, grate, beat

Pages 56–57
Josh's room

Across:
1 mirror; 3 alarm clock; 6 bed; 9 chair; 10 desk; 11 basin; 13 poster; 15 wardrobe; 16 lamp; 18 radio; 19 bicycle helmet; 20 computer; 21 slippers

Down:
1 magazine; 2 rugby ball; 4 mobile phone; 5 personal stereo; 7 plant; 8 window; 10 door; 12 rug; 14 shelf; 17 curtain; 19 book

Pages 58–59
Adverts you love and hate

(1) (Students' own answers)

(2) (Students' own answers)

(3) (Students' own answers)

Pages 60–61
Paintballing fun

1 van; 2 bus; 3 dog; 4 bush; 5 tree; 6 bike; 7 wall;
8 fence; 9 bench; 10 fountain; 11 signpost; 12 lamp post;
13 phone box; 14 litter bin; 15 sports car; 16 motorbike;
17 traffic lights

Pages 62–63
Spot the difference

The ten differences are:
In Picture A, the guitarist has got curly hair; in Picture B, he
has got straight hair.
In Picture A, the guitarist is left-handed; in Picture B, he is
right-handed.
In Picture A, the guitarist is wearing a shirt; in Picture B, he
is wearing a T-shirt.
In Picture A, the singer is wearing a skirt; in Picture B, she is
wearing trousers.
In Picture A, the singer has got long hair; in Picture B, she
has got short hair.
In Picture A, the drummer has got a beard; in Picture B, he
hasn't got a beard.
In Picture A, the drummer has got some hair on his head; in
Picture B, he hasn't got any hair (at all).
In Picture A, the drummer isn't wearing glasses; in Picture B,
he is wearing glasses.
In Picture A, the group is called *Now*; in Picture B, it is called
Wow.
In Picture A, there are three spotlights; in Picture B, there
are four spotlights.

Pages 64–65
A day out in York

(Students' own answers)

Pages 66–67
Spy-catcher

(1)
In the picture:
box, cupboard, desk, drawers, keyboard, lamp, mouse mat,
mug, paper, photocopier, picture, plant, printer, radiator,
telephone, wastepaper bin

Students tick all the items except:
photocopier, cupboard

(2) (Students' own answers)

Pages 68–69
Twenty questions

(Students' own answers)

Pages 70–71
Test your powers of communication!

(Students' own answers)

Pages 72–73
Football reporter

1 began, fouled, kicked; Picture D
2 saw, sent; Picture E
3 took, ran, seemed; Picture B
4 roared, made; Picture C
5 was, passed
6 turned, took, scored; Picture A
7 tried, headed, failed
8 ended, cheered, kicked, missed, won; Picture F

Pages 74–75
Holiday postcards

(1)
1 I really like swimming but the sea is quite <u>cold</u>! C
2 My <u>walking boots</u> are too tight and my feet hurt! D
3 Skiing isn't easy but it's great <u>fun</u>. A
4 We visited this <u>palace</u> yesterday. B
5 There's plenty of snow here because it snowed
<u>yesterday</u>. A
6 I'm going to try water-skiing <u>tomorrow</u>. C
7 I love hiking: we're walking about twenty <u>miles</u> a day. D
8 I like <u>reading</u> my book on the beach. C
9 Many of the rooms were boring but I liked going round
the old <u>kitchens</u>! B
10 I fall over ten times every day but I'm still <u>enjoying</u> it! A
11 We went rowing on the lake in the <u>gardens</u>. B
12 My rucksack is too <u>heavy</u>. D

Page 76
Formula 1

(1) (Students' own answers)

(2) (Students' own answers)

Page 77
Designer clothes

(1)
1 ☺; 2 ☹; 3 ☹; 4 ☺; 5 ☺; 6 ☹; 7 ☺; 8 ☹

(2) (Students' own answers)

Pages 78–79
A school for wizards

(1)
Character: a swot, brave, friendly, generous, good fun,
nasty, strict
Appearance and clothes: blond, old-fashioned, plump,
straight, tall, thin, trendy
Likes: chocolate, dragons, giving homework, lying in bed,
putting spells on people, telling jokes, turning people into
animals

(2) (Students' own answers)

(3) (Students' own answers)

Pages 80–81
A car for everyone

①

1 Sports car; 2 Beetle; 3 Sports car, Smart; 4 Sports car, Smart; 5 People carrier; 6 Sports car, People carrier; 7 Beetle, Smart; 8 Beetle; 9 Sports car, People carrier, Smart; 10 Sports car, Smart; 11 Smart; 12 Sports car; 13 People carrier; 14 Students' own answer; 15 Students' own answer

②

James would probably buy a *Beetle*.

③ (Sample answers)
Sports car: Tara is twenty-four and isn't married. She has a good job. Image is important to her. She likes driving fast and likes to feel the wind in her hair.

People carrier: Mr and Mrs Green have four children and a dog. They carry lots of things around, for example sports gear and musical instruments. They travel long distances on holiday and like to travel in comfort.

Smart: Patrick is twenty-six and single. He doesn't need a big car. He cares about the environment and rides a bike when he can. He wants a car for journeys that are too far on his bike. He likes things with a modern style.

Pages 82–83
TV quotes

①

1 C; 2 G; 3 B; 4 H; 5 E; 6 A; 7 D; 8 F

② (Students' own answers)

③ (Students' own answers)

Page 84
Mystery boy

(Students' own answers)

Note to the teacher:
Students are encouraged to use their imaginations and use the picture as a stimulus. Their answers can be wild or realistic, but their answers should comprise a coherent scenario, e.g.

Where is this happening? (which town? country?)
This is in London.

What has just happened?
The boy has just broken into a jeweller's shop.

What does the boy have under his jacket?
He has stolen some jewellery and is hiding it under his jacket.

Where is he running to/from?
He's running away from the police.

How is the boy feeling?
He's feeling guilty and scared.

What do you think is going to happen next?
He's going to run into another police officer, and he is going to be arrested.

How is the story going to end?
The boy will wake up in his own bed in the morning and find that it was all a bad dream.

Page 85
A strange story

(Students' own answer)

Pages 86–87
Reporting a bank robbery

①

£90 000 was stolen yesterday morning in a robbery at Smedley's bank. A gang of *two* bank robbers entered the bank, armed with *guns*. Their faces were hidden by *scarves*. Three customers were in the bank at the time: they were told to sit down *but* their hands *were not* tied.

One of the bank's employees, *Mr Jones*, was told to hand over the money from the till. *He* was then ordered to open the safe. The robbers' *black* van, driven by the *third* member of the gang, was waiting in the street outside.

The police were called and managed to track down the robbers to a farm. The farm was raided at *midday* and *three* people were arrested: *two men* and a woman. Police dogs were used *and the money* was found.

② (Students' own answers)

Pages 88–89
London through the ages

①

1 C; 2 B; 3 C; 4 A

② (Sample answers)
• **Transport**
B: In the late nineteenth century, people travelled by train.

• **Shopping**
B: In the late nineteenth century, people bought things in different shops.
C: Today people can do all their shopping at the supermarket or over the Internet.

• **Entertainment**
C: Today people can watch videos and satellite television at home.

• **Communications**
A: In the Middle Ages, people had to talk to each other in person.
B: In the late nineteenth century, some people had telephones.
C: Today many people have mobile phones.

• **Clothes**
A: In the Middle Ages, women wore long dresses.
B: In the late nineteenth century, women's dresses were still long.
C: Today many women wear trousers.

• **Buildings**
A: In the Middle Ages, many houses were were made of wood.
B: In the late nineteenth century, there were a lot of brick houses.
C: Today many people live in blocks of flats.

③ (Students' own answers)

Material written by: Gwen Berwick and Sydney Thorne

Project manager: Howard Middle of HM ELT Services

Edited and produced by: Process ELT (www.process-elt.com)

Designed by: Studio Image and Photographic Art - Athens, Greece (www.studio-image.com)

Photos: Rune Hellestad/Corbis for page 22; John Percival/Photolibrary Wales for photo F on page 47; Digital Vision Ltd for page 68; Associated Press/Jockel Fink for page 69; Digital Vision Ltd for photo A, photo B and photo E on page 73; PictureQuest/Alan Brooke for photo C on page 73; Corbis Images for photo D on page 73; David Turnley/Corbis for page 77

Illustrations by: Peter Standley

Published in the UK by Scholastic, 2021
Euston House, 24 Eversholt Street, London, NW1 1DB
Scholastic Ireland, 89E Lagan Road, Dublin Industrial Estate, Glasnevin, Dublin, D11 HP5F

Printed in the UK by Bell & Bain Ltd, Glasgow
Paper made from wood grown in sustainable forests and other controlled sources.

www.scholastic.co.uk/elt